Notorious
CORKS

HISTORY'S
MOST
UNSTOPPABLE
STOPPERS

Chad Crowe

CHAD CROWE
ILLUSTRATION

ISBN 978-1-7374584-2-5

Illustrations and text by Chad Crowe
Design by Brenda Crowe
Photography by Tosha Shelepova

Chad Crowe
www.chadcrowe.com

For Brenda

DISCLAIMER:

This is a work of fiction.

Any resemblance to actual events or persons, living or dead, is probably true.

Corks are the red-haired stepchildren of the wine industry. Wine is always the star of the show. What is the grape? The vintage? The region? Is it oaky, smoky, buttery or grassy? Does it have legs? What dress did wine wear to The Oscars? The cork is the Best Supporting Actor, doing all the grunt work so wine can bathe in the glamorous spotlight of celebrity. Does the cork get any respect? Hell no it doesn't. It is pushed down, screwed out, tossed and forgotten. The most the lowly cork can hope for is to be discovered by some crafty person, have its back slathered in hot glue and slapped onto a cork board or picture frame for eternity.

The unfortunate truth is most corks are unremarkable little plugs with no personality. However, this simplified view also overlooks the many outliers, artists, criminals, bon vivants and revolutionaries that have existed since the first cork was painstakingly carved from a tree by a frustrated Neanderthal. Collected in these pages you will find twenty-five of the most unstoppable personalities to ever stop a bottle: a rogue's gallery of corks for the history books.*

*Please be sensitive with the information disclosed. If the cork is fortunate enough to still be living, there is a good chance it is in the Cork Protection & Witness Relocation Program, and its privacy needs to be respected. Remember: its little life could be in your hands.

BERNARD CLICQUOT

The Freak from Marne

Bernard was scalped in The Champagne Riots of 1911. The saber attack that removed much of his frontal lobe and left him chronically despondent inversely gave him the nose of a savant. Fleeing the burning villages of France, and lacking the cognitive ability to plan his future, Bernard boarded a steamship for America. PT Barnum discovered him, and Bernard joined his traveling circus as "The Freak from Marne," sniffing out the grapes, region and vintage of any glass placed under his sad little face. Bernard quickly became the top attraction, igniting a jealous rage in The Tattooed Lady and Jo-Jo the Dog-Faced Boy. They easily convinced Bernard to be the first "Cork Cannonball" for the 1933 World's Fair in Chicago, filling the small bronze bottle with white phosphorous before packing his little head down. He remarkably survived the explosion, but lost his sense of smell. Bernard now works as a high school counselor.

ENZO DE'MEDICI

The Terror of Florence

Signor Enzo was a sadist. For Enzo, any blend was the perfect accompaniment to whips, chains and pain. The dirty little bastard popped out of Lorenzo de Medici's Barolo in 1490, and lived in the royal house for two years until he bit Michelangelo's ass at a dinner party. Enzo terrorized the residents of Florence for hundreds of years, never knowing if they'd be snatched off the street for a brutal tasting session. His autobiography, "Plugging Holes where the Sun Does Not Shine," published in 1766, caught the attention of the Marquis de Sade, who purchased Enzo as his muse. The years in Chateau Lacoste with de Sade were the happiest of Enzo's life, collaborating on, and writing about, the most depraved wine parties a cork could lay eyes on. De Sade was taken to the asylum in 1778, but Enzo remained in the castle until 2017 when the #MeToo movement finally brought him down.

1659

FRITZ BOOZENHOOT

Oracle of Table Mountain

High above Cape Town on the rocky outcrop of
Table Mountain sat Fritz, South Africa's divine
prophet of wine. For hundreds of years vintners,
sommeliers and wine celebrities made the arduous
hike to seek the Oracle's wise counsel. He was
rumored to have been placed on his perch by the
god Bacchus to oversee the cultivation of South
Africa's vineyards (Fritz was actually just a piece
of litter from a drunk Dutchman in 1659). It
wasn't until the 1980s that Fritz met his downfall.
Stressed owners of wineries questioned how to
consistently produce the "notes of gooseberry and
grass" their customers demanded. Fritz suggested
additives such as MSG, Band-Aids and antifreeze
might do the trick. The resulting hospitalizations
caused a scandal in what became known as
"Gooseberrygate." Fearful of being incriminated, a
cabal of top wine personalities slipped a roofie into
Fritz's chardonnay, covered him in peanut butter
and fed him to a chacma baboon.

GRETA COTSWOLD

The Queen's Cork

Greta was a genius. She had to be, overseeing the royal wine cellars of Queen Elizabeth II. Tucked away under Buckingham Palace, Greta was responsible for managing 35,000 bottles worth over $5,000,000. In addition to selecting the wines for the events upstairs, she also had to service the wine needs of Windsor Castle: the royal fox hunts, "Camillagate" and scandalous pool parties. This would be impossible for most corks, but Greta was gifted with the brain of Einstein and the will of Genghis Khan. Her only soft spot was her intense love for the Queen. When the Queen hired Jancis Robinson, a young tosser from Oxford, to assist her it felt like a corkscrew to the heart. Not only did Jancis have an impeccable resume, she didn't look like a small wooden spark plug with hydrocephaly. Greta's mental health quickly deteriorated. She was fired in 1999 after the publication of her tell-all book, "Wine and Windsor: Fifty Shades of Grape." She now works for Meghan Markle.

HARRY SINGH

The Poker from Punjab

Harry was a Sikh who didn't drink. This was a problem, as he was born with a nose for hedonism and a wine-opener on his head. In 1927 an English chef visiting Amritsar discovered Harry floating in the waters of The Golden Temple, and brought him to London as his little wine servant. His abilities earned him a reputation, and soon everyone wanted Harry's nose, and to get a peep of the legendary corkscrew under his turban. A cork of deep faith, Harry was disgusted with his job, and often followed advice with disclaimers - "A Riesling is the perfect accompaniment to the Tikka Masala, but a shitty pairing for your flatulent soul." The only thing more important to Harry than his job was his honor. When an American diner called Harry a "Bearded Barkfaced Bastard" for refusing to pour a glass of Whiteclaw with her chicken wings, he unpacked his corkscrew and poked out her left eye.
Harry now runs a mini vineyard on the island of Alcatraz.

HOTUSHI YOSHIHIRO

The Seventh Samurai

Hotushi wasn't particularly well-balanced. He was carved from a ginkgo tree in Osaka in 1957, and displayed a remarkable talent for writing wine haikus. He was soon recruited by the"Gang of Seven" - elite Samurai Sommeliers who roamed the world upholding the highest principles of wine stewardship. Hotushi was the most talented. Until he developed a bark tumor and went nuts. He began demanding pairings such as Cabernet with Granola, Merlot with Twizzlers and tawny port with Twinkies. Followed by his elaborate Kabuki theater production "Harakiri with MD 2020," Hotushi became a national disgrace to Japan. The Samurai Sommeliers eventually hunted him down for "re-purposing." Hotushi is now a part of the flooring at The Rokuon-Ji Temple in Kyoto.

IVAN ZOLOTOVSKY

Cork of the Czars

Ivan was a tough little bastard. A Cossack cork from the Black Sea, he terrified vineyards along the Volga with his militaristic wine reviews. Nicholas II, the last Czar of Russia, purchased him in 1870 to oversee his Imperial Wine Cellar. By night Ivan slept in a velvet-lined Faberge egg, and by day overturned wine racks, shattered bottles and cleaved corks to suppress any insurrection in the cellar. 1917 was a bad year for Ivan, when the Bolsheviks overthrew the Czars and cheap fortified wines in the cellar overthrew him. He was sentenced to indefinite house arrest at The Hotel Metropol for "Crimes Against Affordable Wines." In 1952 an undercover agent discovered Ivan at the hotel bar, glued a recorder in his cap, and he became the CIA's "Cork in Moscow." He was accidentally swallowed by Boris Yeltsin in 2007.

JOSE MENDOZA

The Malbec Maniac

Jose was the cork on Che Guevara's Molotov cocktail. His scabby nose, riddled with bullets and shrapnel, would sniff out the best cigars for Che during the Cuban Revolution. The two met in 1951 when the young revolutionary uncorked him from a cheap bottle of Malbec on his legendary motorcycle ride north. The trip changed Jose, and he vowed to never plug a bottle of "capitalist grape rot" again. After the revolution, Fidel Castro hired him to detect potential US assassination attempts. Exploding pens, razors and cigars were all easily discovered by his talented sniffer. In 1980 Jose inserted himself into a C4-packed bottle of Havana Rum in an attempt to blow up Ronald Reagan. En route, he fell out of the plane and floated to Key West. Jose was placed on a shelf at Sloppy Joe's Bar, and is still waiting to be ordered.

KARL WEINSCHWEIN

Canceled King Karl

Karl was often considered the most interesting and magnificent cork of all time (although a few thought he was a misogynist little prick). Karl emerged from a bottle of Grauburgunder in 1806 with a godlike talent for cocktails and bar aesthetics. His mind-blowing redesign of Munich's Hofbrauhaus jump-started his spectacular career crafting cocktails and bars around the world. Every classic drink, from the Sazerac to the Martini, and every famous bar, from El Floridita to Studio 54, had the mark of Karl's teeny hands. His book "The Gentleman's Complete Guide to Getting Shitfaced," is considered The Bible of the bartending world and has been translated into every language on Earth. Scandal erupted in 2017 when Karl was discovered in a back room of the Tiki Ti bar with cheap screwcaps snorting packets of Columbian non dairy creamer. He now works as a greeter at Wal Mart.

KERMIT O'LEARY

Doctor Feel Good

Kermit popped into the Summer of Love in 1967. The unofficial cork of The San Francisco Flower Children, Kermit had tried every inhalant, benzodiazepine, cannabinoid, opioid and barbiturate, but had a special love for psychedelics. After an arrest for public nudity, Kermit was forced to attend an educational course on viticulture at Berkeley. Kermit developed an insatiable fetish for wines from southern France, and soon began pairing them with psychedelics. Kermit's "Chateauneuf-du-Pape and Ayahuasca" retreats were highly controversial, but earned him a James Beard Award in Experimental Intoxicants. It was when Kermit began demanding the Surgeon General label "Wine + LSD = Ecstasy" that the government cracked down. When they raided his lab, Kermit disappeared in a Beaujolais-Peyote explosion. He is rumored to be living in Marseilles and has won every French national award of merit.

DR. KHATIA RHEINHESSEN

The Sex Doctor

Khatia was a sex psychologist. Having spent the better part of a decade trapped in a bottle of Riesling on Sigmund Freud's shelf, Khatia learned everything she needed to know about the id, egos, Oedipus Complexes and the effects of cocaine on an elderly Austrian man. When Freud finally uncorked Khatia in 1939, he was stunned to not only find a talking cork, but his intellectual superior. Concerned what the Nazis might do, he plugged her back into a bottle of Gewurztraminer and shipped her to Stanford University, where she immediately earned a PhD in Psychology. Khatia found the experience of being plugged and uncorked strangely thrilling and penned her breakthrough thesis on "Uncorking Sexual Desire: Bottle Friction and the Liberation of the Mind." This led to her 1980s call-in talk show "The Freudian Sip," giving advice to sexually confused wine stoppers. She now hosts the popular podcast "Corkscrewing the Joy out of Life."

1943

LIZ
BIRD

Enemy of the State

Liz wanted to burn down the patriarchy. Despite rampant sexism in the cork industry, her gifted nose shattered the glass ceiling when she became the first female sommelier of New York's Algonquin Hotel in 1943. Liz not only had to select wines for a constant stream of manspreading, mansplaining half-wits, she had to do it with a smile, so as not to offend their sensitive dangling grapes. Over the years, Liz's resentment grew. She began holding secret meetings for "The Sisterhood of the Vine" at The Chelsea Hotel, leading other corks in writing feminist wine reviews and very tiny bra burnings. Their self-published "Put a Plug in Patriarchy: Wine Pairings for The Anarchist's Cookbook," became an underground sensation, and also caught the attention of the FBI. Accused of being communist corks "soaked in Karl Marx Cabernet," Liz and her friends were sentenced to ten years of "re-education" making Blizzards at Dairy Queen. Liz now teaches Comparative Literature at Columbia University.

MAXIMILIEN D'BALTHAZAR

The Executioner's Nose

Max was a psychopath. A noble cork from Versailles, Max was hired to be the Wine Vicar for Paris' first fancy restaurant, La Grande Tavern des Londres. Perched on a bottle of Bourgogne, he orchestrated wine pairings for the Paris elite like a conductor. In 1789 he smelled the whiff of Revolution, and feared his own fine coiffure might fall under the guillotine. Max penned a manifesto to the revolutionary Maximilien Robespierre, declaring "Wine is filled with Noble Rot, and the Reign of Terror needs a Reign of Terroir." The two quickly became known as "Max 'n' Max" pairing seized royal wines with public executions. Screams of "Out with the corks and off with their heads!" filled the air as the streets ran red with blood and Bourgogne. He disappeared in 1794, but is rumored to have recently been spotted singing Bob Dylan tunes at the Saint-Lazare Metro station.

MIKEY O'HEFFERNAN

The Wild Cranberry

Mikey was a cork from County Cork with severe mental health issues. He popped out of a bottle of Bunratty Mead in 1916 only to be shoved in another bottle, lit on fire and thrown at terrified police officers. Decades of therapy and reconstructive surgery followed, and a metal cage was necessary to hold Mikey together. It wasn't until he was singing Irish lament songs in the Central Criminal Lunatic Asylum that the world discovered Mikey's pipes. A long career followed, touring with every major Irish band from The Dubliners to The Cranberries. Unfortunately, the cage could not contain the rage. After being denied a Grammy for his a capella rendition of "Zombie," he bit off the judge's finger, screamed "Bono is a lickarse!" and his head exploded into flames. Mikey's charred little corpse now rests under the floorboards of Murphy's Pub in Dingle.

1984

ROD SUCKLING

Naughty Rod

Rod was a cork from Detroit. His wine education began with plugging bottles of Mad Dog 20/20, the sugars of which made his hair grow. His fame blossomed when he began pairing cheap wines with 1980s rock ballads, and landed a position as Chief Sommelier at General Motors. Thirsty autoworkers would ask such questions as, "Does Iron Maiden bring out the subtle tannins in Night Train?" Or "Will pairing Loverboy with Boone's Farm make me lucky?" for which Rod always had an answer. Success lead to excess. After hours he liked to be placed on the stick shift of a Camaro, and persuade female autoworkers to pet his hair to John Parr's "Naughty Naughty." Fearful of a PR nightmare, GM glued Rod to the hood of a parked Yugo and he safely disappeared for two decades. Rod now tours high schools giving presentations on the dangers of toxic masculinity.

OMAR AL-BAALBEK

The Dreamer

Omar just wanted to design women's shoes. He'd spent hundreds of years plugging bottles of Merlot, Cabernet and Syrah in Lebanon's Bekaa Valley, but dreamed of a life in Paris watching beautiful models strut down the runway in his elegantly crafted stilettos. "A little hole-plugger is all I'll ever be," he thought. Until 2008, when he plugged a bottle at a Tony Robbins "Unleash the Power Within" event in Byblos. Omar's little fibers ignited with inspiration. He smuggled himself to New York in a bottle of tahini and painstakingly earned his BA at The Fashion Institute of Technology, followed by an MA in Shoe Architecture at Harvard, a 3-year unpaid internship with Manolo Blahnik, and a PhD in Molecular Female Footwear at MIT. Twelve years later and $752K in student debt, Omar graduated during the COVID-19 pandemic and couldn't find a job. He now works for Amazon in Newark, NJ.

PEPE CERVANTES

Cork of La Mancha

Pepe Cervantes is old. In 1547 he was cut from a tree in La Mancha to plug the tonic bottles of a mad surgeon/barber. Purchased by a wealthy, wine-loving aristocrat from Seville, he oversaw a massive cellar while perched atop the finest bottles in Spain. This boosted Pepe's ego and eventually led to grandiose delusions. Convinced he was a member of The Cork Knights of Andalusia and "Fermentation Dragons" were trying to infiltrate the wine cellar, he would lance about with a corkscrew shattering the hallucinations he saw inside the bottles. Unfortunately this became a chronic problem. The Spanish king exiled Pepe and he washed up on the shores of Algeria where he was forced into bondage as a prison wine steward. He returned to Spain after miraculously escaping in a freed prisoner's body cavity. He was last seen in 1987 eating a lobster on the roof of Salvador Dali's home in Cadaques.

1839

PIERRE DEPARDIEU

The Paris Screamer

"CHIANTI TASTES LIKE CAT PISS!" was a phrase Pierre commonly screamed. When Pierre popped out of a Veuve Clicquot bottle in 1839, he was considered to be the most eloquent and sophisticated cork in all of Paris. As a Celebrity du Jour, he traversed the city as an obscenely well-paid sommelier for the most wealthy houses of Paris. In 1858 an aphid landed on his hat and he contracted phylloxera, resulting in a severe case of Tourette's. Yelling "THAT CROISSANT GONNA GIVE YOU HEPATITIS!" at fancy French ladies wasn't very helpful for his career, but screaming "YOUR MUSTACHE IS LONGER THAN YOUR PECKER!" at Napoleon III was considered treason. To drown out his filthy screams, Pierre was locked in the bell tower of Notre Dame and forgotten. That is, until the fire of 2019. Pierre was evacuated to a new life as a tourist attraction on the Champs-Elysees, where he can now be found screaming obscenities at travelers from around the world.

REZO SAPERAVI

The Drunk Poet of Tbilisi

Rezo was a poet and a drunk. He was found in 1902 when archaeologists heard him singing inside an ancient Georgian Qvevri, and dated at over 6000 years old. He instantly became an attraction at the taverns of old Tbilisi. When placed on a bottle, Rezo would inhale the contents within seconds, followed by the most sublime poetry a mortal could hear. An audience was brought to sobs of despair or cries of joy simply by placing him on a bottle of Saperavi. In 1937 Rezo was even forced to sing to Joseph Stalin, raising that heavy mustache into a smile and narrowly escaping life as a Siberian wine stopper. Thousands of years of intoxication finally caught up to Rezo. His exquisite poetry was replaced by expletive-laden rants against gentrification and digital nomads. His rage-filled haranguing at a social media influencer in 2019 caused the gin blossoms on Rezo's nose to detonate, and he vanished in a hot orange flash.

1947

ROB HIWALANI

Point Break Rob

Rob Hiwalani pissed a lot of people off, especially the French. Rob began his career in 1947 after popping off a bottle of Guava wine on Oahu's North Shore. It was there he learned about wine and Big Wave Bottle Surfing from tourists who were convinced Rob's little pig nose was blessed by the god Pele himself. To fund his surfing addiction Rob began a point-based rating system which he mailed in his newsletter Big Wave Wine Advocate. Almost overnight Rob became the world's most influential critic, and wineries knew anything below a "Hang 7" rating spelled doom. The French were enraged at being subject to this simplified rating approach and revolted against "Le Hiwalanization" of the industry. Rob disappeared after attempting to surf a magnum of Dom Perignon during Hurricane Iniki in 1992.

1946

RONALD MEINFOORER

The Plug of Putin

Ronald was rotten the moment he popped out a bottle of cheap champagne on 725 5th Ave in New York. From an early age, Ronald grew long wispy golden locks to hide his putrid insides. Despite this, he considered himself the "most genius and stable wine stopper of all time!" The owner of The Russian Tea Room, amused by Ronald's outbursts, placed him on a mini bottle of Cook's Brut for the diners' entertainment. Screams of, "Your wine pairings are for losers!" and "I alone can make wine great again!" brought howls of laughter from the crowds. With his surging popularity he demanded to be placed on larger and larger bottles, but even the massive Melchior wasn't enough. In his insatiable thirst for power, Ronald incited a takeover of the restaurant. He fell from the bottle in the ensuing riot and his parted hair revealed his hollow insides. Ronald disappeared before he could face trial, and is rumored to be Vladimir Putin's personal suppository (a trendy new approach at wine tasting).

RUDOLPH WANG

The Bogus Bordeaux

Rudy was a fraud. He popped out of a tree in Jakarta in 1976 with grand dreams, but ended up plugging bottles of industrial alcohol. His big break came when he escaped in the suitcase of an American businessman traveling to LA, and learned about the world of wine. However, his nose was much better at smelling profits than tannins. Rudy began gluing labels of Chateau Lafite onto jugs of Carlo Rossi Sangria and making millions at auction houses. It was only when he began slapping labels of Chateauneuf-du-Pape onto boxes of Franzia that people began to smell the cork taint. In 2012 he was arrested and immediately deported to France. Rudy's head is currently impaled on the entry gate of the Chateau Lafite Rothschild estate.

SETH

Nose of the Pharaohs

Seth was pulled out of Amenhotep II's crusty nose in 1898 by Egyptian tomb raiders. Sold into the cork trafficking circuit, Seth plugged cheap bottles of hooch from Alexandria to Ouagadougou. But Seth knew he was a descendant of Shezmu, the God of Wine. He had served every Pharaoh from Zanakht to Hatshepsut, selecting their ancient beer collections, sniffing out assassination attempts and overseeing the giant wine press used to crush the skulls of their enemies. Amenhotep II loved Seth, shoving him up his left nostril upon death to serve as his personal cork in the afterlife. To be taken out of that royal nose, and forced to listen to the vapid conversations of silly people using words like "oaky," "bold," and "hints of tobacco" was too much for Seth to endure. It was at a wine fair in Tonopah, Nevada, in 1982 that Seth finally invoked the Wrath of Shezmu. Nothing happened though, because nobody believed in Egyptian gods anymore. Chinese billionaire Peter Tseng bought Seth at auction for $100K where he now sits on a shelf amid a collection of adult toys.

VITO BUFALINO

The Cork of Corleone

Vito was so evil he was rumored to have been belched out of Mt Etna's 1949 eruption (in truth he was pried out of a rancid Nero D'Avola bottle by the notorious Luciano Leggio). Adept at smuggling, and prone to bouts of extreme violence, he was hired by the Corleonesi to collect protection money from the vintners of Sicily. Over time the bottle-detonations and cork-suffocations were enough to convince them that Vito meant business. In the 60s he was promoted to cigarette smuggling and the 70s to high-profile political assassinations. By the time the unwitting politician had corkscrewed out Vito's smiling head, they would never notice the tiny hands holding the Tommy Gun mowing them down in a stream of bullets. His luck ran out in 1990 when he was arrested in Manhattan for attempting to smuggle a bottle of cocaine-filled cannolis for John Gotti's birthday party. After serving 20 years, he now works as a highly paid consultant in Hollywood for mob movies.

YVETTE KAHN

The Wrath of Kahn

Yvette had a premier cru pedigree. Popped into life at the Chateau Mouton Rothschild estate in 1853, Yvette received an elite education in French viticulture, carving her into the most sophisticated cork in France. She wrote fifteen cookbooks, edited 27 journals and received hundreds of awards, earning her the title "La Grande Tête du Vin Français." The title was lost in 1976 with "The Judgment of Paris." As one of the premier judges on a blind tasting competition between American and French wines, she was enraged a bottle of "cheap California plonk" was declared the winner. How could grape juice from a land of nouveau rich, bucktoothed barbarians beat out the noble blood of Bordeaux? Her screams of "PUTAIN FRAUD!" were met with mild laughter. Bubbling with rage, Yvette brutally attacked an American judge with a day old baguette. Yvette can now be found placed in restraints on a bottle of Charles Shaw at a Napa Valley Trader Joe's.

About the Author

Chad Crowe is an illustrator who knows much more about drawing silly pictures then he does about wine, but apparently knows a great deal about corks.

Acknowledgements

Special thanks to Brenda Crowe for the layout of this absurd book, Tosha Shelepova for the professional photos, Peter F. May for his knowledge and expertise, and Josh Flenniken, Bem Jimmerson, and Erik Pierce for their helpful suggestions and support.

Brenda Crowe
brenda-crowe.squarespace.com

Tosha Shelepova Photograpy
imtosha.myportfolio.com

CPSIA information can be obtained
at www.ICGtesting.com
Printed in the USA
BVHW022102301121
622514BV00049B/226